Barkve

D1472843

Katarina Hellner

Joan is Angry

Illustrated by Tineke Daalder

HODDER AND STOUGHTON

LONDON SYDNEY AUCKLAND TORONTO

British Library Cataloguing in Publication Data

Hellner, Katarina
    Joan is Angry.
    I. Title
    839.8′1′37J   PZ7.H/

    ISBN 0-340-23872-0

Copyright © 1978 Leif Stegeland Förlag AB, Göteborg.
English text copyright © 1980 Hodder & Stoughton Ltd.
First published in Great Britain 1980.

Printed in Italy for Hodder & Stoughton Children's Books,
a division of Hodder & Stoughton Ltd,
Mill Road, Dunton Green Sevenoaks, Kent TN13 2YJ
(Editorial Office: 47 Bedford Square, London WC1B 3DP),
by New Interlitho, Milan.
Photoset by Rowland Phototypesetting Ltd,
Bury St. Edmunds, Suffolk.

My name is Joan and I'm nearly seven. Sometimes I think I'm very grown-up, but sometimes I feel very small. When I'm angry I feel very small. Do you feel angry sometimes?

"Joan, put your clothes on," said Mum.
"Here are your jeans and your sweater."
"I want my dress with the flowers," I said.
"You are going to wear that one for Sandra
and Peter's wedding on Saturday," said Mum.
"But I want to wear it *today*. Mary and I are
having a wedding in the cycle shed. I *must*
have it," I said, very determined.
"No," said Mum, even more determined.
"YES, YES, YES," I screamed.

4

"Well, put it on then," said Mum. "Just wear it to your wedding in the cycle shed. If the dress gets covered in oil or catches on one of the bikes and tears, don't worry about it. We'll just sit at home watching the telly instead of going to the wedding. Dad can tell us all about it afterwards. They're going to have ice-cream there, so Sandra tells me."
Then I thought I ought to think it over again for a while.
"Mum," I said when I'd finished thinking. "I'll put on my jeans and sweater – just in case it's cold outside."

5

Mary and I were playing with our balls in the garden. My ball was big and red. Mary had two little balls. Every time I dropped mine Mary took it and started playing with it. In the end I lost my temper.

"LEAVE MY BALL ALONE," I screamed.
"IT'S MINE, ISN'T IT?"

Mum came into the garden. She took Mary's
balls and played with both of them at the
same time. It looked so funny.
"Let me try, Mum," I asked.
"You'll have to ask Mary," said Mum.
"They're her balls."
"Mary," I said, "if I can borrow your little
balls, you can play with my big red one."
"OK," said Mary. "We can change again
after a while."

Mary and I were on our way to the shop. We were going to buy some ice-cream. There was a long queue, and we had to wait. When it was our turn, a man said, "I just want a paper."

"It's our turn," I said, "and we're in a hurry."

"Hurry," snapped a woman. "Children are never in a hurry. All they do is to play all day. May I have some liquorice?" she asked the shopkeeper.

"We're buying ice-cream to take home," I said. "Actually."

"Aren't children cheeky nowadays?" the woman said to the shopkeeper. "And a bag of fruit drops."

I was so very, very angry that I could have kicked that woman really hard. I could have kicked her to the moon.

"It just isn't FAIR," I shouted.

"Listen, pet," said a man beside me. "I think that lady must have a really sweet tooth. Let her buy her sweets so she can go home and gorge herself."

"Well I never! Such cheek!" said the woman.

"Oh, I'm sorry," said the man. "I forgot you were only allowed to be nasty to children. I think it's your turn now, sweethearts."

"You can have a lick of my ice-cream," I said to the man.

Mary, Rose and I were skipping in the garden.

"Wrong again," shouted Rose.

"I know, I know," I snapped. "I'm wrong because you swing the rope so badly."

"I don't swing it badly, do I, Mary?" shouted Rose.

"'Course not," said Mary. "It's Joan who's all wrong."

"It's the rope that's rotten," I screamed. "I'm not playing if we're going on with this rotten old rope!"

"Don't play then," shouted Mary.

"Skipping is so boring, don't you think, Mum?" I said when I went indoors.

"It is for me, because I can't do it very well," said Mum. "Do Mary and Rose find it boring?"

"No, because they can do it," I said, sulking.

"Well," said Mum, putting me on her lap. "How did they learn it?"

"They've practised all summer!"

"Then you'll have to start right away."

"But I get so very ANGRY when I make a mistake, you see."

"Yes, I see. Don't Mary and Rose ever make mistakes?"

"Oh yes, but I make the most. But today I didn't make as many as yesterday."

"There you are! It helps to practise," said Mum. "I suppose all three of you need practice."

"I'll take my new skipping rope!" I said to Mum when I went out again. "The other one was rotten!"

10

"Do you know, Mum," I shouted when I came in again. "Mary has got a new doll. It can talk!"

Mum was talking on the telephone. "I want an appointment with Doctor Jones," she said, and waved me away.

"But listen, it can sing, too, and it has yellow hair with a bow!" I said.

"S-s-s-s-h!" whispered Mum. "Wait a moment."

"I don't want to WAIT," I screamed. "I'm talking to you NOW!"

"Friday? Thank you very much," said Mum to the telephone, and put it down. She looked very angry indeed!

"I heard you," she shouted. "But I've also got things to do that can't wait. You must UNDERSTAND that! I've not always got time to spare exactly when it suits you!"

"Are you very angry?" I whispered.

"Yes," said Mum. "Just as angry as you! I think it helps me to shout when I'm angry. It's all over more quickly. Do you understand?" she said, and hugged me.

"Yes," I said, "I'm fit to burst when I'm angry. I want to bring it all out in the open. Once it's out, I feel much better."

"What was it you were going to tell me?" asked Mum.

"Mary has a doll that can talk," I said. "It can sing 'Mary had a little lamb'. Can I have one, too? We could go and get it right away."

"No, darling," said Mum. "You've got three dolls already. And you hardly ever play with them."

"Rose and Louise have got dolls that can talk, too," I said. "ALL THE OTHERS HAVE! I'M THE ONLY ONE WHO HASN'T." I felt really angry.

"Do you think we are going to get a new house just because we scream?" asked Mum.

"But you've got tons of money," I sulked. "You can just go out and buy one."

"You've got money in your piggy bank," said Mum, "but there's not enough for a talking doll. Dad and I have some money in the bank. But it's not enough for buying a house. We'll have to save a little longer, the three of us."

"BUT ALL THE OTHERS HAVE," I screamed.

"THE ROBERTSONS HAVE A SAILING BOAT," shouted Mum. "WE HAVEN'T! Because we'd rather have a summer cottage. Don't you think it's nicer to buy something you'd like to have rather than to buy because all the others have it? What do you want most of all?"

"A horse," I said. "We could keep it in the big wardrobe. Just a pony, because they're so small. You'll get me one, won't you, Mum?"

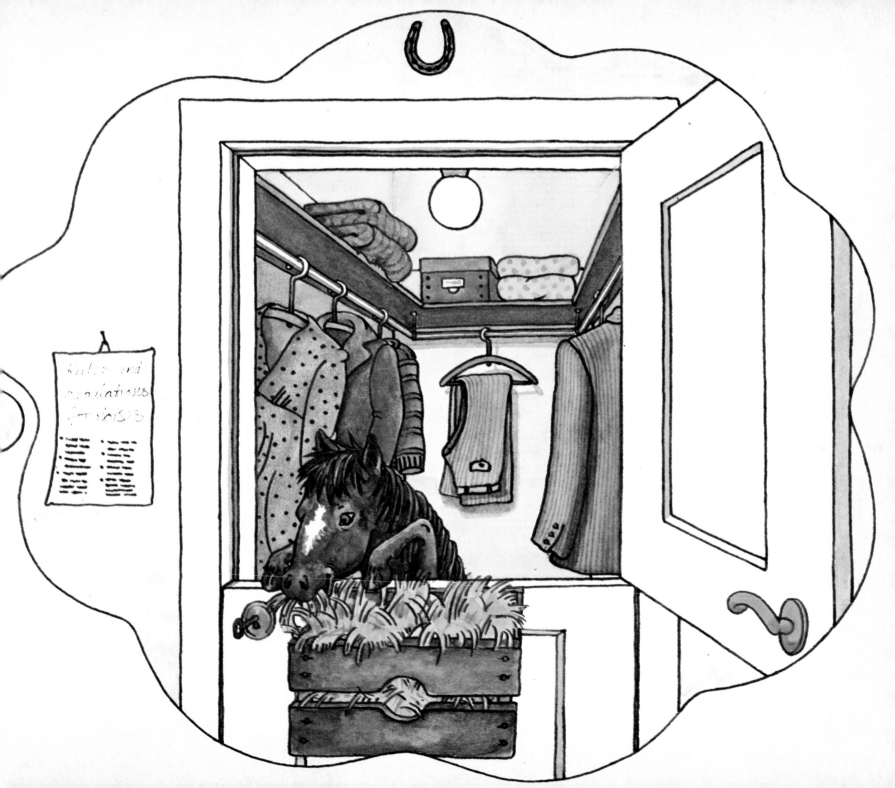

Mum and I were going out shopping.

"I want to sit in front with the safety belt on," I said.

"No," said Mum. "Children sit in the back. Hop in."

"But Peter is allowed to sit in the front," I said angrily. "Isn't he a child, too?"

"Yes, but he's eleven," said Mum. "Hop in the back now."

"He IS still a child, and he's allowed to!" I mumbled, and glared at Mum. "It's not fair!"

"Sit in front," said Mum.

"Oh Mum, you *are* nice," I said when Mum put on my safety belt. "Let's go to Smith's shoe-shop."

"We're just going to try something," said Mum, and leaned forward. "Can you see that my belt comes across my chest, even when I slide down on the seat a bit?"

"Yes, what about it?" I asked.

"Slide down a bit, Joan," said Mum. I did so, then Mum gave me a little push in the back. The belt came down across my throat.

"What are you doing?" I screamed. "I choke when you do that!"

"No you don't," said Mum, "but if I had to brake hard, or if something ran into us, then you would. I want you to sit in the back, because you are safer there. Do you understand?"

"Yes," I said. "There's a lot more room, too, actually."

Dad and Nigel were at home when we got back. Nigel is my big brother. I showed them my new shoes.

"Kid's shoes," said Nigel. "Only babies wear shoes like that."

"I am BIG," I screamed. "I'm going to be seven soon."

"Ha-ha, I'm NINE!" shouted Nigel. "And when you are nine I'll be eleven!"

"BLAH!" I shouted and put my tongue out. "YAH BOO!"

"What's all the noise about?" shouted Mum. "What's the matter with you two?"

"I shall never be the same age as Nigel," I sobbed and cried. "Why does he ALWAYS have to be the OLDEST?"

"Well, what can we do about that?" she said, and put me on her lap.

"Give him some poison so that he dies," I said.

"Nigel, stop teasing Joan at once," said Mum. "I'm a few years older than you. Do I tease you because of that? Isn't it childish to go on the way you are doing?"

Nigel looked ashamed. I felt very smug.

"You're childish, you're just a baby." I felt on top of the world. "Isn't he, Mum? *I'm* not childish! I'm almost seven – SOON!"

"JOAN," said Mum. "If I can scold Nigel I can scold you, too. Nigel IS nine years old and you ARE seven – SOON!" And she went out of the room.

"Baby," whispered Nigel.

"MUM, Nigel's teasing me!" I shouted. "He called me a baby!"

Mum rushed in. She threw a book on the floor in front of us.

"What's that? What kind of book's that?" asked Nigel.

"It's called UNDERSTAND YOUR CHILD," shouted Mum. "But the people who wrote it have never met you two! Love and explanation doesn't help, it seems. So now I couldn't care less if I understand my children. They don't understand me! GO TO YOUR ROOMS!"

Sometimes it's quite nice to be alone. You can sit and wriggle your toes and think. I was thinking about a big brother who didn't tease me. He was very nice and sweet, like a dog. Then I started thinking about a dog. "DINNER TIME! WAKE UP!" Dad was standing in the doorway. My dog had just met a small frog. Dad's shouting made them so frightened that they ran away.

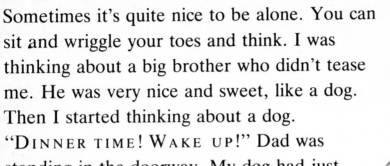

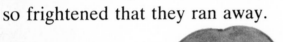

I was so angry that I marched out into the kitchen. "*You* want to be alone sometimes," I shouted, "but what about me? Dad is allowed to shout in my room so that he scares my dog away."

"Have you got a dog in your room?" asked
Dad.
"No, in my head, silly," I sniffed. "But it's
gone now."
"I'm sorry, darling," said Dad, and wiped
away my tears. "I didn't know you were
sitting there thinking. We'll write a notice
saying I AM THINKING and put it on your
door when you want some peace. How about
that?"
"Lovely! Because I do a lot of thinking, you
see!"

Nigel and I were building with bricks. We were having such fun!

"Bedtime, Joan," said Dad.

"We're just having such a good time," I said. "Can't I stay up a bit longer?"

"No," said Mum. "I'm running your bath. You can play with the bricks again tomorrow."

"But that's not NOW, and I'm having FUN!" I howled. "I always have to go to bed when I'm having FUN."

Mum helped me undress and put me into the
bath. "You also like having a bath," she said.
"Not so much as building with bricks," I said,
sulking.

"It was silly of me to take you away from
your building so suddenly," said Mum. "But I
could see you and Nigel were having fun, and
I thought you could play until your bath was
ready. Dad and I are very tired, so we want
you and Nigel in bed, so that we can go to
bed, too."

"It's funny," I said. "You can hardly ever notice when grown-ups are afraid or when they are sad. But you can see when they're angry. And HEAR it!"

"Sometimes when grown-ups look angry, they may just be afraid or sad," said Dad. "There was a time when boys were not allowed to show they were afraid or sad. But they were allowed to show anger. Girls were not allowed to show they were angry. But they could cry. Those girls and boys are now grown-up Mums and Dads. Mum and I think that we should all be able to show it when we're afraid or sad or angry."

"But I'm only angry sometimes," I said.
"So are we, fortunately," said Dad, and laughed.